Classics of Modern Chinese Literature

A **Xu Zhimo Reader**

Translated by Fu Hao
Illustrated by Jing Wei

Printed in China

中国国家汉办赠送
Donated by Hanban, China

 CHINA INTERCONTINENTAL PRESS

Classics of Modern Chinese Literature

A Xu Zhimo Reader

图书在版编目（CIP）数据

徐志摩：英文 / 徐志摩著；

傅浩译 .— 北京：五洲传播出版社 ,2013.11

（中国儿童名著精选译丛）

ISBN 978-7-5085-2652-2

Ⅰ．①徐… Ⅱ．①徐… ②傅… Ⅲ．①儿童文学－作

品综合集－中国－现代－英文 Ⅳ．①I286

中国版本图书馆CIP数据核字(2013)第256446号

出 版 人：荆孝敏
作　　者：徐志摩
译　　者：傅　浩
插 图 作 者：京　惟
责 任 编 辑：张美景
装 帧 设 计：缪　惟

出版发行：五洲传播出版社
社　　址：北京市海淀区北三环中路31号生产力大楼B座7层
邮政编码：100088
发行电话：010-82005927, 010-82007837
网　　址：www.cicc.org.cn
制版单位：北京锦绣圣艺文化发展有限公司
印　　刷：北京天颖印刷有限公司
开　　本：889mmx1094mm　1/32
印　　张：5
版　　次：2013年11月第1版　2013年11月第1次印刷
书　　号：ISBN 978-7-5085-2652-2
定　　价：89.00元

Biographic Notes

XU Zhi-mo (1897-1931), poet and essayist, was born in Haining County, Zhejiang Province, China. He was educated at University of Shanghai, Peiyang University and Peking University. During 1918-1922 he visited the US and the UK as an overseas student. From 1924 on, he taught at Peking University, Kwang Hua University, the Great China University and Central University. Meanwhile, he was a co-founder of the Crescent Moon Bookstore with Hu Shih, Wen Yiduo, etc, and the editor-in-chief of the *Crescent Moon Monthly* and thus a representative figure of the Crescent Moon school. He died of an air crash. His publications include 4 books of poetry, 3 collections of essays, 1 collection of short stories, 1 play and many translations.

FU Hao is a research professor of English at the Institute of Foreign Literature, Chinese Academy of Social Sciences. He has published 2 books of poetry, 1 collection of essays, 4 books of literary criticism and 23 books of translated works from world literature.

To William Harmon,
a friend in need,
whose assistance in improving
my translation is invaluable

contents

ESSAYS

POEMS

REVERIE AT THE SEASIDE OF BEIDAIHE[1]

They all went to the seashore. I did not go because of an inflammation of my left eye. I sat alone on the front porch, installed in a big comfortable armchair, with chest exposed, feet bare and hair dishevelled by the fitful breeze. The clear coolness of the morning had not refreshed me, just out of bed, but half of my dreams were

---

① Beidaihe is a seaside resort on the northeast coast of China.

1

Xu Zhimo

disturbed by the morning wind. Drooping my
eyelids and looking inward, I saw spots of faded
colours, just like the remainder of evening twilight
clinging to the edge of the sky, seemingly reluctant
to leave. The green leaves and red blossoms of
the silk trees, judas trees, and wisterias all cast
their graceful shadows on the waterside, weaving
various charming patterns, and my arms and
chest were fully covered with the slant lines of
the shade. The bay could be seen directly through
the intervals between the trees: the sea seemed
also awaken by the morning twilight, dancing
delightedly with yellowish and bluish glints. White
surf rose by the beach now and then, scattering
foam like snow. Within the line of the bathing area,
tiny forms of boats and bathers floated like water
birds; children's joyful shouts, sounds of waves
splashing on the sand and undercurrents groaning
rose and fell, intermingled, competitively reporting
the liveliness and pleasure all over the beach. But
around the porch on which I sat alone, there were
hardly any sounds. The charming silk tree flowers
just quietly opened a little bit, and even flies and
gnats folded their wings. Only the autumn cicadas

2

among the trees far and near were spinning their endless chants.

Among the endless chants, I sat alone meditating. It was rare to have such a lonely place and such a peaceful mind; there were indescribable harmonies in the loneliness and limitless creativeness in the silence. My mind was like the seashore, on which the first swells of the tide in my life had gradually passed away one by one, with but occasional echoes left among the loose sands, and broken seashells reflecting moonlight and starlight. Now fumbling for the traces in the aftermath of the tide, I recalled the uproar then, which, being dreams or realities, did not need to be questioned any longer, but the slight frown of my eyebrows and little smile on my lips were sufficient to explain numerous causes deeply rooted in the fibre of the soul.

A youth always tends to rebel, loves adventures, dreams of golden chances beyond vast oceans like the sailor going to sea for the first time: longing to cut the cable, hoist the sails, and gladly plunge into the embrace of the infinite. He hates peace and safety and likes self-indulgence and heroics. Colourless life is a thorn in his side, while boundless seas and dangerous peaks are the paths to freedom he loves. He loves to gather roses not only because of their colours and smells but also of their cruel stinging thorns. He loves to fight the fierce waves not only because of their sublimity and greatness but also because of their talent for devouring everything, which most stimulates his motives of exploration and curiosity. He worships impulse, which, unpredictable, uncontrollable and irresistible, starts, acts and ends all formlessly, like a storm, swift, violent and mysterious. He worships struggle, in which he seeks the meaning of tumultuous life and absolute being , and hails victories with joy or laments losses with elegies on blooded battlefields.

The disappearance of visions is a tragedy predetermined in life. A youth's disillusionment is the tragedy of tragedies, dark as night, murderous as death. Unlike Aladdin's lamp, pure and wild fire of passion, can only give out a momentary light, but not shine forever, and in a moment, maybe, has its last flames put out, with only a limited amount of remains and ashes left, pitying and comforting itself in the remaining warmth.

The lights of streams, stars, dewdrops and lightning are reflected in the young beautiful eyes. We cannot help marveling over the mystery of the Creator's art, but at the same time the horrible shadows of weariness, decay, and complacency follow the days closely, like the tails of sorrow, distress, loss or mediocre, and like the meteors sweeping up the glory we are mostly proud of – streams, stars, dewdrops and lightning, all gone.

In the brilliant sunshine, there are pleasure, dancing and liveliness. Hope, twinkling hope, is hopping among the endless blue skies, the lustre of green leaves, the singing of birds and insects, the waving of grass – summer's glory and spring's achievement. Spring and hope are everlasting; nature and life, harmonious.

In the blessed valley far away, primroses smile on the slope, lambs leap among rocks, some of the young shepherds play reed pipes, and others lie back on the grassy ground, looking up at the floating and changing white clouds that cast bluish shadows, which move lightly, across the yellowing rice fields. In the pleasant village far away, a rustic

Xu Zhimo

lass looks at the reflection of her home-made skirt for the springtime in the stream, three or four farmhands smoking pipes calculate in advance how big the autumnal harvest will be, and several old women sit outside the doors of their own houses to warm themselves in the sun, with quite a few children about them, dancing and shouting happily around with yellowish coins in their hands.

In the world far, far away, there are limitless peace and happiness, endless spring glory...

Here I could momentarily forget the numberless fallen pistils and petals, or the goodwill of the dead leaves that predicted in a whisper the coming of autumn in the shade of flowers, or the sorrowful

6

and deadened people whose lively smiles on their faces could be no longer restored by the dancing attendance of sunlight and rainwater, or the conflicting and mutually murdering ones whose murderous bestial natures could not be softened by the benevolence of sunlight and rainwater, or the mediocre, low and base ones whose gaze could not be attracted for a moment by the gracefulness of the floating clouds and morning dewdrops, or the self-conscious and despaired ones whose sad feelings could only be increased by the splendid springtime and graceful grass.

I could also momentarily forget everything

about myself: the innocence of my childhood that was like a cool breeze and clear water, or the vain expectations of my boyhood, or the gradual awakening of my life, or the passionate pursuit of my ideals, or the struggle between optimism and pessimism in my mind, or the difficulty of my climbing the summit of art, or the mystery of momentary revelations and enlightenment, or the sudden turns in the course of my life, or the good or ill fortunes of my falling into perilous vortices, or the dreams I could not recall completely, or my secrets that buried their heads in the bottom of the sea, or the sharp edges that cut my soul and ferocious flames that burned my soul and violent storms that destroyed my soul, or my bitter complaint and deep resentment, or my hopes and wishes, or my patronage and indebtedness, or my past and my present...

The past realities gradually inflated, blurred, and became unrecognizable; the present ones gradually contracted and narrowed into a line in consciousness, a thinnest line, which in turn broke into numerous discontinuous black dots... which, in turn again, faded away one by one? Perished,

perished like illusions. A terrible dark void...

1924

Xu Zhimo

SUNRISE VIEWED FROM MOUNT TAI

Zhenduo[1] wrote to me, asking me to write something on Rabindranath Tagore for the special issue of *Fiction Monthly*. I had agreed, but recently I have been too excited – touring Jinan City, Mount Tai, and Confucius' Tomb[2] – to collect my thoughts to write the whole piece. So I have not tried to piece together what I wanted to say until now, with the deadline near.

We viewed the sunrise from the summit of Mount Tai. To one who has been at sea, it is no special experience to watch the sun climbing up from under the horizon, and I myself have been sated with the incomparable grandeur of the sunrise over the Yangtze and the Indian Ocean. Nevertheless, viewing the sunrise from the summit of a high mountain, especially on that of Mount

---

[1] Zheng Zhenduo (1898-1958), writer, founder of the Society of Literary Research, was then the editor-in-chief of *Fiction Monthly*.
[2] Jinan City is the capital of Shandong Province in eastern China. Mount Tai and Confucius' Tomb are also located in Shandong Province.

Tai, we certainly, to satisfy our curiosity, expected a special kind of spectacle different from the view from plains or seas. Indeed, at the time when we got up, it was still dark, jet black in the west and slightly pale in the east, and the whole firmament – an old expression – in total darkness. But that was only my vague judgment as I was still half awake in the bitter early morning cold. When concentrating on looking around, I could not help crying out wildly – for in front of my eyes there was a scene never seen before. Last night's storm had created a vast sea of clouds, reaching all around the Peak of Sun Sight and the Summit of Jade Emperor, and which, before the morning sun emerged, resembled sheep in woolly fleece sleeping side by side and neck on neck, with their rolled ears and curved horns dimly recognizable. At that time among the vast sea of clouds, standing alone on the small misty island, I had a wonderful vision –

My body had grown infinitely big, and the mountain underfoot compared to my height was only a stone as big as a fist. This giant, with long loosened hair all windswept like a huge jet black flag, stood upright on top of the earth, looking

Xu Zhimo

up eastward with both long arms raised to the horizontal, expecting, receiving, urging, silently calling, worshiping, praying and weeping – with warm tears out of the mingled feelings of sadness for not having seen it after long admiration and joyfulness for being about to see it...

The tears were not in vain, nor the silent prayer unanswered.

His hands pointed towards the east –

What was there to be shown in the east?

In the east there were majestic, glorious colours, and grand omnipresent light – appearing, coming and being here...

Rose extract, grape juice, judas tree sap, agate marrow, frosted maple – a large quantity of dye worked under the multi-layered clouds; numberless swimming fish and snaking dragons crept into the heaps of pale clouds.

The special colours in a quarter removed sleep from all over the sky and woke the twilight in the four corners of the world – the godly colts of light were galloping exhilarated...

The sea of clouds also came to life. The waves in the various shapes of beasts after sound sleep recovered their great howls and rushed towards our scone-shaped islet dyed blue by the morning dew, fashioning foam and froth around the shore, rocking the lively floating reef, as if announcing the coming of light and joy...

Look at the east then – Hercules had wiped away all his hindrances, and the golden glow like a peacock's tail risen from his boundless shoulders, spreading on the edge of the earth. Up... up... come on, come on! The round head of pure flames jumped out of the horizon on its first or second try, climbed on the backs of the clouds and looked

down from the summit of the heavens...

Oh, sing, oh, praise. This is the renaissance of the east. This is the victory of light...

The giant praying with loosened hair and casting his shadow on the boundless sea of clouds had gradually dissolved in the universal joy and now the resonant sound of his singing hymns had reached all quarters in the changes of the multihued clouds...

Oh, listen to the universal cheers! Oh, look at the universal light!

That is my reverie at the moment when I recalled the sunrise viewed from Mount Tai and my hymn to Tagore to whose visit to China I am looking forward.

1923

IF I COULD FLY

If now there were snow outside the window – on the streets, city-walls, roofs, all snow; a policeman in a black-visored cap cuddled up under the eaves of a house at the top of the lane, with sleepy eyes half closed, looking at the cotton-like snow dancing in the air... If the night were the deepest, not deep as the hands of the clock hung on the wall show us, but deep as a cave spiraling downward...

If I could have such a night, whose bottomless gloom make my hair stand on end, and the snow outside the window, whose nonstop falling makes the noise of the market fade away, the wheels struggling in the mud disappear and the uncompromising undercurrent in my mind die out...

I want that depth. I want that quietude. The owl hiding in the shade of thick leaves usually dare not come out and open his eyes in broad daylight.

Xu Zhimo

Thought has to wait, too.

There was a black spot in the blue sky. You could not see it clearly just facing the blinding sun. Shade your eyes with your hand and look through between those two trees. It's black, as big as an almond, no, as a peach – oh, it's moving westward.

After lunch we went out to the seaside (it is the furthest cape at the end of Cornwall, England, surrounded on three sides by the Atlantic Ocean). A series of chirping sounds rose from underfoot steadily up, trembling, to the waist, the shoulder, overhead, into and out of the clouds. Ah, can you imagine a kind of fast reverberating musical sound as a shower of drizzling light coming out of the blue sky continuously down to the green matted ground? No, the raindrops are all tiny dancing feet, of angels'. The skylarks also had had their lunch, and left their humble nests on the ground for a higher place to do the work given by God for God. Look, one here, and two up there! They flew towards the summit of the sky as soon as they took off. How lively their little wings move, revolving, in unhesitant flight – what they know is the blue sky. They began to sing as soon as they took off. How lovely their little voices sound, like round delicate beads spat out continuously, crisp, crystalline – what they praise is the blue sky. Look, how high they fly. Some were as big as beans, and others as sesame seeds, or black dust particles, all floating towards the bottomless summit of the sky – now all vanished without a trace! But the drizzling rain of light was still falling...

Flight. "Whose wings are like the clouds hung in the air... Who bears the blue sky on his back and of

Xu Zhimo

whose progress no one could get in the way"[①] – that
is not easy to be seen. There is a yellow clay hill
out of the eastern gate of our town, and a seven-
storey pagoda, whose spire touches the heavens,
on top of the hill. The bell often rings in the
monastery where the pagoda is. When it sounds,
which occurs mostly at sunset, a big beautiful red
flower stuck on the temples of the west hill shines
back on the clouds over the pagoda hill; when
it sounds, around the spire, across the sky and
through the clouds above the pagoda, one or two,
sometimes three or four, sometimes five or six,
"hungry hawks" with curled claws, looking down
at the earth's surface, seemingly carefree, spread
their big grey wings wheeling, floating in the air,
drifting in the evening wind, as if practicing a
waltz to the sound waves of the bell in the pagoda
monastery. They were the "rocs" of my childhood.
Sometimes when hearing the whistles in good
cloudless weather, we knew that the hungry hawks
had come from the pagoda to seek for food. Once
the bald and round-eyed heroes in the air came
into our mind, with feathers like iron brushes

---

① Quotations from *Zhuang Zi (Chuang Tze)*, a Daoist classic dated 3rd
century BC, chapter 1.

Xu Zhimo

growing from our shoulder blades, which rustled while being shaken, we rushed in an instant out of the classroom into the white clouds with turtle-shell hems to play. Who would stand patiently before the teacher's desk reciting from memory the difficult text that we had learned in the morning! Ah! Flight! Not the flight of the sparrows hopping among the low branches; nor of the bats rushing out from behind the inscribed board hung in the hall at dusk to hunt mosquitoes; nor of the swallows with soft tails and voices who build nests under the eaves of the hall. If I could fly, it must be a flight across the sky, one that cannot be hindered by winds and clouds, and that crosses a mountain top with a single flap of the wings, and that can cover twenty acres of rice fields with a shadow cast down, and that circles round the pagoda in accord with the wind direction, dreaming after a day's tiring expedition... It is said that the hungry hawks grab chickens!

Flight. Originally all men could fly. As angels have wings that can fly, so did we in the beginning. At first we flew here. Some had flown back having accomplished their mission. They are admirable. Most, however, forgot how to fly. Some could not fly any longer because feathers had fallen off their wings and grown no more; some, because their wings had been stuck together with glue and could be separated no more, some could only hop on the ground like pigeons, because their feathers had been trimmed short; some had pawned their wings for cash at the pawnshop and failed to redeem them because the lease had expired... Indeed, we have lost our ability to fly as soon as childhood passed. But it is terrible that your wings are lost or unusable because of being broken, for you can fly back no more. How pitiful you are, who crouch on the ground gazing dispiritedly at the sky you cannot climb and who watch blessed others enjoying themselves among the bluish clouds round after round. And unlike the shoes you wear, of which you can ask for another pair after they are worn out, the wings cannot be mended once they have lost their feathers, even single one. Moreover, it is uncertain when you can fly merely with the aid of your wings; is it not also hard that your wings will not have enough strength to lift you up if you imprudently put on too much weight? What a ridiculous scene that a pair of small wings cannot bear a fat belly! At that time hearing someone call out, Hey, buddy! Go back home before the purple glow in the sky disappears, and the rustle of their flapping wings in the air and seeing them, spring clouds on their shoulders and backs, in the brightest direction of whence they came, fluttering and drifting like wisps of smoke, vanish from sight, like the skylarks leaving behind only a shower of light – "Thou art unseen, but yet I hear thy shrill delight"[1] – you alone will remain in the mud. How sad, how sorrowful and how disgraceful! Mind your wings as early as possible, buddy.

No one does not want to fly. How boring to crawl on the ground, let alone other things. Fly out of here, out of here! Into the clouds, into the clouds! Who do not think so hundreds of times a day? Fly into the sky, floating, to see the ball of the earth rolling in the space, from land to sea and from sea to land. To see clearly in the air – it is a

---

① From l. 20 of the poem "To a Sky-Lark" by the English poet Percy Bysshe Shelley (1792-1822).

human being's interest, authority and purpose in life. Cast off the body if it is too heavy to move. If possible, fly out of here, out of here!

Humankind has wanted wings since he first invented stone implements. He wanted to fly. The beast painted on the wall of primitive man's cave has wings on its back, and he who chases the beast with a bow and arrow also has wings on his shoulders. Eros has a pair of white fleshy wings. Icarus is the first hero and victim in the history of human flight. The primary mark of angels (that are idealized human beings) is their wings with the help of which they fly. There is a process of development too – look at the representations in western paintings. At first the wings were like a pair of small well-wrought pennons stuck on the backs of the angels who looked like butterflies, seemingly real, but lifeless. Gradually the wings have grown bigger, in place and full feather. The angels in the paintings have got real potential wings. Man has realized the concept of wings for the first time and fully understood the meaning of flight. The undying soul of Icarus' flashes back to be born and reborn. The greatest mission of mankind is to make wings; the greatest achievement, to fly! The ultimate in ideals, the finality of imagination, from men to gods! Poetry is born on the wing and philosophy hovering around in the air. Fly: out of all, over all, excluding all, including all.

Go to the mountain top over there to try. If you fail to fly across to this side, you will have to find your burial place in the ten-thousand-metre-deep valley. "One day the human-shaped bird will try its first flight, shock the world, make all writings praise it and give everlasting glory to the resting place from where it came."[1] Oh, Da Vinci!

But to fly? Since Icarus, has man's work been to make or bind wings? Can the wings be used to fly once they are loaded with the burden of civilization? Can everyone still fly back who flew here? Clipped, welded, pressed, will the human-shaped bird have its day to try its first flight?

Meanwhile, the black spot in the sky got near over my head, becoming a bird-shaped machine.

---

[1] Unidentified quotation. In other place, however, the author mentioned and translated a chapter from a novel *The Romance of Leonardo da Vinci* (1928) by a Russian author named [Dmitri S.] Merejkowski.

Suddenly a ball of light fell down from one side of the machine, bang, a blast – my flight of fancy broke into pieces, there were more heaps of fragmentary floating clouds in the blue sky.

1926

Xu Zhimo

FALLEN LEAVES[1]

The day before yesterday your Mr. Zha[2] called to ask me for a lecture, and I said that I had nothing to say and that I was most impatient with lectures. He said, just come, speak as you please, as freely as you please, and just say whatever you want to say. As you know, we have had a hard time since this semester began, and our students led a dull and boring life, so we want you to come to give us a little water for survival. Those words moved me. What is dull and boring, I understand. Although I am not acquainted with you, the fact that you feel life is dull and boring has immediately begotten a kind of true and deep sympathy between us. I know what a formless and unreasonable monster dullness is. When it comes, our body seems wholly covered by a large cobweb, out of which we have

---

[1] This is an extract from a lecture given at Peking Normal University in the autumn of 1924.
[2] Zha Liangzhao (1897-1982), Dean of Studies at Peking Normal University then.

hardly got one arm when the other is stuck inside. That is a horrible web. I, too, know the ugly face of dull life, and you also, I think. It is everywhere, possessing everyone, and presenting itself on everyone's face. Look at your friends. There it is on their faces. And look at yourself in the mirror. There it is, too, on your face, I think. Terrible dullness, a kind of poison, once it has got into our blood and humours, our skin changes colour, which, I afraid, is one that is far from life and near to the grave.

I am one who believes in feeling, and maybe myself a born man of feeling. The other day, for instance, the west wind came. That morning when I woke to the coldness, the colour on the paper

windowpanes looked lighter than usual, my limbs wrapped in the quilt were like being immersed in cold water, and I heard the dry leaves of a date tree were blown down by the wind in fits and starts, rolling on the ground, rustling, some having flown out of the courtyard and others remaining swivelling in the corner with a sound like sighs. Hence it came into my mind that since the west wind had woken me up from my dreams and blown down the leaves of the tree, its achievement in a world of the ordinarily poor and hunger-stricken must be extraordinarily considerable. When I went out that day, I did see the situation on the streets was quite unusual. All the poor old men and children cuddled up together in street corners shivering. Sooner or later they could not escape the fate similar to that of the dry leaves on the tree. Then I felt it was particularly dull, almost miserable.

Therefore, when Mr. Zha told me how dull and dry your life was, I understood fully and would like to come to speak to you. My thought – if I have any – is always unsystematic. I do not have that kind of talent. The movement of my mind is impulsive, or even convulsive. When thoughts won't come, I can't make them come; but when they come, I feel as bad as if I am in a wet shirt, and have to do something to get rid of them. I have an analogy. Just now I mentioned the dry leaves in the autumnal wind, and I may well liken my thoughts to the leaves on the tree, which will not fall until the time comes, but which have to fall one by one when the wind comes with the time. Most of them may be already lifeless, dry, and yellow, but a few may still retain a bit of autumnal colour. For example, maple leaves are red, crabapple multicoloured. The leaves definitely do no good, but some, such as myself, have a fondness for fallen leaves. Some of them bear a bright colour having just fallen down, but after a long time the colour changes unless you preserve them well. So my words, that is, my thoughts, are as useless as fallen leaves, and sometimes at best bear a few traces of the colour of life. You who do not like them may as well tread on them heedlessly; a minority of people who have a natural affinity with me, however, may not blame them for their uselessness but pick them up and hide them in bosom or books, attempting to keep their fading colours. Feelings, true feelings, are rare, dear and fit for sharing. We should not reject nor oppress feelings, for that is a crime, the same crime as stifling a spring or suffocating a child. A person in a society is originally an unrelated individual. Feelings, innate and acquired, are the threads, the warp and the weft, that form the originally separate individuals into a patterned whole. Sometimes, however, the threads may become loose or worn out, so there must be new ones continuously produced in a society, to mend the worn-out or tighten up the loose part, so that the whole could be generally kept in good condition. Sometimes if there is a special rise in production, we will have a chance to expand or make a supplement to our existing area, or strengthen our existing texture like threading a tennis racket with double layers of strings, because we know that the forces of creation and extermination, construction and destruction, God and Satan, coexist. Those two forces are weighed against each other on the same scales, and they seldom keep a balance, tipping either to one end or to the other. Yes, human destiny is weighed on the huge scales, looked on there by a huge black shadow that is our collective incarnation, who adds a handful of weights now to one end, now to the other. The earth turns on, the sun, moon and stars shine in turn, and our fate is always weighed on the scales.

Just now I mentioned the tennis racket. Right, it is a good metaphor. You who play tennis know which strings of which part of the racket receive the most impact and therefore are the most important. When those strings are particularly strong, not only are your chops, drives, and smashes exceptionally effective and spectacular, but your racket is also exceptionally hard-wearing. A minority of particularly strong elements keep the whole in good condition. To apply that principle to human life means that if we are able to concentrate and strengthen our commonest strings of sympathy, and if the strings can be threaded through all the beating hearts, our big net will be firm and hard-wearing, or as the Tianjinese[1] say, rooted. No matter how bad the weather is, rainy, cloudy, frosty or windy, no matter how fast the stream

---

[1] The native of Tianjin, a port near Beijing, the capital of China.

flows, only if we have such a strong big net, can't we, sooner or later, in the endless tide of time net some priceless valuables, or add great weight of creative life to our fate on the scales?

That's why I'd say true feelings, human feelings, are valuable, and that they are the fundamental elements of a society. At first it may be an accidental vibration in one's heart, which, however weak it is, makes a far-reaching ripple, which, if it causes sympathetic reactions, will become thick from thin, strong from weak, tough from fragile, like many ramie fibres twisted into a thick rope – originally a ripple, now a wave; formerly a thread of water in a valley, now a big river rolling towards the boundless seas. Jesus' Sermon on the Mount, for instance, has only a limited number of words, but such a short speech has defined the ultimate state of human expectation, established the absolute standard of values and invented a pure and perfect religion. That is a great event, one of the greatest in human history. Again, for example, Sakyamuni, in order to find out the truth of life, age, sickness and death, out of great compassion, perseverance and fearlessness, forsook his high worldly status, wealth and rank, family and wife, to practice asceticism in the mountains, with the result that he has also opened up a great path of liberation for the miserable world and given the most glorious definition of genius for the eastern peoples. Isn't the origin of such great events merely an accidental vibration in an individual's heart, merely a drop of most transparent true feelings fallen down in the dark universe?

Feelings are power, not knowledge. The human heart is a warehouse for power, not for logic. A representation with true feelings, no matter what it is, a work of poetry or prose or music or sculpture or painting, is like a stone thrown into a calm lake. You can see the change it causes while standing still. The lifeless theory, no matter what it may concern, is a stone thrown into a desert, only adding a dry particle to the dry land. Except that it may make some dry noise as it is thrown down, there is only a vast deathlike silence. So, only feelings are the springs that form rivers and the threads that can be woven into a big net.

But how about our own net? Now is the right time for us to open our eyes wide and clearly see the truth about what is happening around us. We have been equivocal for a long time, and shall be no longer. Let us announce loudly that our net is broken, worn out, and decayed; let us announce straightforwardly the bankruptcy of our nation, with its morals, politics, society, religions, arts, and everything. Our hearts have become worms' homes, and in our souls lies a big terrible lie. It is the weight of extermination but not that of creation, the force of destruction but not that of construction, and Satan's evil power but not God's holy spirit that tips the balance. In a moment, here the road is full of thorns, there the way cut off by floods, above us there are horrible sounds, thunderbolts or mortar shells? and around us those of weeping and laughing, weeping because our souls are insulted, laughing because the survivors are mad, sounding more horrible and miserable than ghosts' weeping. When we look with opened eyes, there is almost none of the clean lands which has not been flooded everywhere with blood and tears, let alone a safe place, for even if you have forgotten the outside world, you cannot escape from your own sorrow and distress. Don't think that such chaos is caused by economic inequality, or political unsteadiness, or a minority of people's uncontrolled ambitions. All those are empty and deceiving theories that are easy to talk about and that sound pleasant, because we wish only to unload our own duties. Only if I have no part in it, I have the right to blame others. But that, I'd emphasize, is a cowardice act, and that is what I called the big lie lying in our souls. Did you say that a minority of soldiers or rich people were the cause of the present chaos? I'd say to you now: you are wrong, sir, you are totally wrong. You flatter the minority and despise yourself too much. In the universal sunlight let us acknowledge together our own sins, our own impurity, our own ignobleness and cowardice and meanness. We are as dirty as the dirtiest and as ugly as the ugliest. We ourselves are the very causes of our own fates. We will not be saved unless we uproot the big lie in our souls. We will burn the devil with the fire of prayer, we will wash away the devil with tears of confession, and we will have the courage to bear the sins. Once you have the courage to bear your sins, you have the guts to fight against them. There will be no second way out. If you could forgive me for my boldness, I would like to read you a recent poem of mine, for this poem is a more concentrated representation of what I have said today:

I. POISON

Today is not my singing day, when I have a evil smile on my lips, nor my chatting and laughing day, when I have a gleaming blade with me;

Believe me, my thought is evil because the world is evil, my soul is dark because the flames of the sun have been extinguished, my tone is like that of the owl among graves because all the harmony has been destroyed in the world, and my voice is like that of a ghost who is scolding his foe because all the gratitude has made way for all the hatred;

Believe me, however, there is truth in my words though my words are like poison, and truth is never equivocal though in my words there seem the twin-headed snake's tongues, the scorpion's tail, and the centipede's antennae. Because my heart is filled with tenderness, compassion, and love stronger than poisons, more vicious than curses, wilder than

flames, and more mysterious than death, my words are poisonous, cursing, burning and void;

Believe me, all our standards have been buried in the grave sealed up with coral clay, which cannot even be penetrated by the strongest smell of the offering meals: all the standards are dead;

All our faith is like a broken kite hung on the branch of a tree, its broken string in our hand: all faith is broken;

Believe me, the great black shadow of doubt, like a dark cloud, has covered all the interpersonal relations: sons no longer weep for their newly dead mothers, brothers no longer hold their sisters' hands, friends become enemies, watchdogs turn back to bite their masters' legs: yes, doubt has overwhelmed all. Sitting by the roadside weeping, standing in the streets, peeping inside through your window, are all raped virgins: in the pond there are only broken gaudy lotus blooms;

In the filthy stream of humanity, like floating algae, five incomplete corpses, which are Love, Righteousness, Morals, Wisdom, and Credibility, are drifting towards the seas of endless Time;

The seas are restless, with waves wildly rolling,

and on the white crest of each wave is clearly inscribed Greed and Bestiality;

Everywhere are scenes of rape: Greed grips Righteousness, Doubt presses Sympathy, Cowardice flirts with Courage, Lust plays with Love, Violence abuses Humanity, Darkness treads on Light;

Listen, all the licentious noise; listen, all the cruel noise;

Tigers and wolves are in the bustling markets and lively streets, robbers and bandits in your wives' beds, sins and evils in your deep souls...

II. WHITE FLAG

Come, follow me, with a white flag in your hand – not one on which are written the words to instigate hatred and encourage killing, nor one marked with impure blood, nor one on which are painted confessions and curses (Paint your confessions on your heart);

You stand in line, silent, solemn, like a funeral procession, not a trace of colour nor a smile allowed on your faces, solemn, silent, like a file of soldiers for the last-ditch fight.

Xu Zhimo

Now's the time to raise the white flag in your hand like raising your heart, and to look up at the blue sky overhead as attentively and anxiously as looking at your own soul;

Now's the time for you to shed your tears that have been suffering from being blocked, breaking and boiling, straightforwardly, wildly, freely, heartily, waywardly, like a spring out of the narrow valley and like a torrential downpour...

Now's the time for you to howl with your swallowed, oppressed, struggling and surging voice, straightforwardly, wildly, uncontrolledly, ferociously, like a hurricane howling among the sea waves and as you do when you have lost your dearest ones...

Now it's time for you to make your recovered nature, which is purified with the hot-oil-like tears and woken by the thunder-like howling, confess, silently, long and deeply, like cold starlight shed on a lone vale, and like a nun in black kneeling before a gilt shrine...

In the boiling of tears, the full vigor of howling and the silence of confession, you have seen God's everlasting power.

III. BABY

We are looking forward to the happening of a great event. We are waiting for the birth of a sweet baby –

Look at its mother who is suffering in her child bed!

Her stillness, softness, and loveliness of a young woman are now transformed into incredible ugliness in fierce fits of pain: look, the veins all over her body under the thin skin swell violently, terribly blue and purple, like frightened water snakes swimming swiftly in the ditch alongside the rice field, beads of sweat stand on her forehead like beans, and her limbs and body are violently twitching, wriggling, stretching, twisting, as though the mat under her were woven with needles and the bed-curtain around her made of flames;

A still, calm, dignified, and lovely young woman is now transformed into a devilishly horrible thing in the cruel fits of pain: her eyes are now closed tight, now opened wide, which were like bright stars reflected in a pond in a winter night, and which are spitting green and yellow flames, and whose pupils

like glowing red hot coals are mirroring the last fight of her soul; her mouth and lips which were red are now like the cold ashes at the bottom of the stove, shivering, pursing, distorted, not allowed a breath of peace by Death's passionate kisses; her hair is dishevelled, across her mouth, over her bosom, like tangled flax, and a few stray hairs gripped between her fingers;

This mother is suffering in her child bed –

But she is not in despair yet. Her life is trying hard with every fibre of blood and flesh and bones and limbs on the edge of the high cliff to resist and fight against Death's approach;

She has not given up yet, because she knows (her soul knows!) that the pain is not without reason, because she knows that a seed of life greater than herself, a baby longer-lived than everything, is growing in her womb;

Because she knows that the pain is a sign that the baby demands to be born, a forecast that the seed is exploding into a beautiful life in the soil, a signal of the time when she is to accomplish her own life's mission;

Because she knows that the endurance will be

Xu Zhimo

fruitful. In a faint out of the agony, she seems to have heard God's voice answering men's prayers, and angels' voices in praise of the coming light;

So she endures, resists, fights... With every fibre of her being she would redeem the life stirring in her womb. In the expectation of a perfect beautiful baby's birth, she feels the sharpest and deepest pain has become the sharpest and deepest pleasure...

Perhaps that is a senseless wish, but who would not live on? Even if on the verge of despair, we still hope in vain an arm of Hope extended from darkness to support us. We have to consider the painful present to be a preparation for a more glorious future. We are looking forward to the birth of a white plump lively baby.

Recently there were a couple of events that touched me deeply. Let me tell you about them.

The other day a flag-raising ceremony was held at the Russian legation, and I went to see it. Karakhan[1] stood on the platform, smiling slightly, a blue glow of seriousness radiating from his face.

---

[1] Lev Mikhailovich Karakhan (1889-1937), Russian diplomat, was then the ambassador of the Soviet Union to China.

I felt his personal dignity as he watched the rising flag with his head slanted up and that he was at least a man of courage and strategy, and that he was determined to sacrifice himself for the ism. At least there was no trace of carelessness on his face. Meanwhile on the flagpole on the roof gradually arose a piece of shiny red against the cloudless deep blue sky. That new flag was flapping restlessly in the wind. The unusual colour and sound aroused an unusual feeling in me. Was it timidity, pride, or contempt as now the red flag first faced such a great nation of ours? There was applause from some of those present, but intermittently, and that, I thought, could be counted as a sort of respect as we first saw the red flag, but was it out of contempt, pride, or shame? The red is a great symbol of one of the greatest periods in human history, not only standing for the achievement of the Russian nation's bleeding but also setting an example of daring for mankind. In the sound of the flag's flapping I not only seemed to hear the shouts of defeat and victory of the Slav nations of the latest decade, but also imagined the fever of the French Revolution over a century ago, the

Xu Zhimo

madness when the Parisian citizens stormed the Bastille on 14 July 1789. Liberty, equality, fraternity! Fraternity, equality, liberty! Hear, in the shouts the flames of human ideals leaping up from the ground to the summit of the heavens. There is no more important and radical turning point in history. Carlyle in his *History of the French Revolution* used three famous sentences to describe that great event. He said, "To describe this scene transcends the talent of mortals. After four hours of world Bedlam it surrenders. The Bastille is down!" The storming of a prison for political prisoners might not have been counted as something great, but there is something symbolic in the event. The Bastille stands for the force that blocks liberty, and the Parisian citizens' storming of it the struggle of the whole human race for liberty. The "down" of the Bastille is an evidence of human ideals' victory. Liberty, equality, fraternity! Fraternity, equality, liberty! The French people shouted wildly over a century ago. The sound of their shouting is still echoing in human souls. Don't we seem to hear it even after an interval of more than a century. Now the murderous Bastille stands in our way again.

Xu Zhimo

Every iron nail in its gate has almost pierced our hearts and breasts if we are not to go mad.

That is one thing. The other is my impression of Japan where I escorted Tagore in June. Seven years ago when I crossed the Pacific Ocean, I had been to Tokyo for several hours. I remember that I went to Ueno Park to look down at the city of Tokyo from a hilltop and that I got a view of prosperity and exuberance with masses of tall buildings. This time I went to Ueno and viewed the city of Tokyo again. The difference was too great! Houses, yes, there were, but formerly they had been tall buildings of several storeys, and quite a few famous buildings, such as the Imperial Theater and the Imperial University. This time what I saw, it's piteous to say, was only row upon row of temporary shacks made of thin pine planks, white and loose like a beggar's favic scalp, no longer the former view of prosperity and exuberance. Nine tenths of the city was devoured by the great earthquake and burnt down. Usually the earth's surface on which we stand could not be any harder and firmer, but when she turns her body a little or opens her mouth slightly as she please, it would be too much for our fragile life and civilization. We in China can hardly imagine there in the world, the woken but not the dreaming one, should have been such a great catastrophe. We Chinese people do live in catastrophes, flood, draught, war, robbery, and all, but I dare say all our catastrophes put together would not equal the one our neighbour encountered a year ago. The terrors of that event, I dare say, have exceeded the limit of human patience. Some in our country should think it a good thing and that it served the Japanese right. I really would like the doctors of the Concord Hospital to X-ray them to see if they have no hearts. Because in the face of the terrible fate, the whole human race is merely a flock of sheep encountering a rain storm in the mountains; where then is space for racial, political, and other kinds of prejudice? I am telling you something here, because you who have not seen it for yourselves cannot help but be somewhat distanced geographically though you have read about it in great detail in newspapers. Before and after going to Japan to have a look myself, I have had totally different views. Let us assume, just try to imagine, that we getting together here today,

Xu Zhimo

you who is listening and I who is talking, would be gone forever with the platform and the house from the surface of the earth within three ticks, like magic, without a trace, if that trick of Japan were played on us. That is fact. Several five or six-storey buildings in Yokohama collapsed to ground-level in three or four seconds, all gone. As you know, at the time when great disasters happened as the Holy Scriptures described, not only the naturally fragile human beings had completely given up all their vanities, but the most savage beasts and birds also had instantly changed their natures, tigers coming to cuddle up to you like kittens and eagles with sharp beaks going to hide in the hen house, tamer than chickens. At that time of unusual change, when they seemed also to be aware of the relationship that all were living creatures and that all were small worms deprived of resistance to God's wrath, there was sympathy between those of the same fate. Just think of the fact that only in Tokyo two or three million people and the fruits of nearly a hundred years of labour suddenly faced the Last Judgment. Even today when we imagine the scene that their city was like a pot of boiling oil

then, the formerly prosperous marketplace having
turned into a burner with radiant flames, in which
the amassed fruits of human physical and mental
labour all became fuel, in which art, education,
politics, society, man's bones and flesh and blood
all became ashes, and the cries of thousands of
people's, male and female, young and old, which
themselves could shake heaven and earth – when
we just sit on chairs and imagine the incredible
scene without experiencing it for ourselves –
aren't we more or less horrified? That is not for
fun. One probably needs to be at least as talented
as Homer or Shakespeare to describe such an
unusual incident. Suppose you were experiencing
it personally, what would you think then? Would
you still hate your foes? Wouldn't you forgive
your friends still? Would you grip your personal
possessions as usual? Would you have another
chance to cheat others? Would you have any hope?
Why not hold the creature by your side, no matter
whether it was your wife, your father, your servant,
your mother, your enemy, your maid, your cat, or
your dog, send out all the remaining light in your
soul, and in the universal darkness unite with your

Xu Zhimo

fellow sufferer for the last time?

...

1924

PLANTING A FLOWER ON THE BEACH[①]

Friends are luxuries. True friends understand (not fair-weather ones, who cannot be counted as friends). It is not easy for true friends to understand each other. You have to open your own heart in order to open other persons'; you have to put your own heart into other persons' in order to keep theirs in your own. The two-way communication of true hearts or feelings is the secret and pleasure of friendship. But this means that your inner strength is great enough and your spirit lively enough to open and flow at any time, like the spring in the mountain, into some understanding canal that can hold you. Sometimes you have to take a risk, to pay the price and try desperately and patiently to find a path through rocks and thorns, which is likely to be hard, painful, and time-consuming, before your

---

① This is a lecture given at the Attached Middle School of Peking Normal University.

heart, flexible and soft as water, can in search of understanding find peace and joy.

Therefore I said that friends were luxuries and that "understanding" a precious thing, but that one had to swap all one's true feelings for it, or invest them in it. So I dare not talk freely, because I myself know my resources are limited, and the most prudence can hardly let me off being afraid of bankruptcy. I cannot "spend" them freely. The day before yesterday some young friends came to ask me to talk to you, and their sincerity has convinced me to do their bidding, but little friends, I am ashamed to ask, what do I have to give you?

First I want to say something childish, because you are all children. But where am I as a child? I seemed to be a child yesterday, but have changed somehow today. What would a child be but for a little lively childishness? But childishness is like a tender shoot in the clay soil, which may become hard and inhibit its growth when the weather is cold – where to find the warm spring wind in such days?

The child is gone. What you remember is only an unclear shadow, very blurred indeed, which I am recalling as incompletely as a blind person does his own countenance. Even if he could not help but imprint a mask on his hands, that is a death mask. Really gone. One day I saw a little kid who, needless to say, was so lively that he now ran uphill, now climbed trees, now skated on the lake, now rolled in the hay, or just laughed foolishly jumping. Looking on I admired him and wanted to do the same playing with him, but I couldn't, because I am an adult in a long robe harbouring decencies and so afraid of being laughed at that the reserved phoniness has been substituted for the natural liveliness – the child, the child is gone. What is left is just a body eaten empty by age and education, death stiff, unnatural.

I also want the barbarian in our nature back to talk to you, because barbarians are near to nature too. I was deeply impressed when several years ago I passed through India, where the streets, houses, natives' skin colour, look, and way of living were simple, poor and understated, but accorded everywhere with nature – the blue sky above, the hot sun, the yellow caked clay, the tall coconut trees – their tones, colours and structures looking consistent in meaning, like a perfect work of art.

Xu Zhimo

Somehow, that day, having seen their streets, ox-drawn carts, an old driver with shiny bald head and purple round belly, their temples with holy images and flowers offered before the shrines, I felt uneasy inside, as if the scene was a familiar voice calling on you to follow it. Wouldn't your soul like to answer brightly, "OK. I'm coming "? But no, again there was something in your way to prevent you from answering the liberty suggested by the call. What imprisoned you was your education. At that time I felt as bad as a snake that could not free himself from the tough skin that imprisoned him – the barbarian was held down too, never to get out.

So I who am standing before you today am no longer a barbarian in harmony with nature, or a child naturally lively. I am merely a "civilized man," and what I can say is merely "civilized words." But what is civilization but degradation? The civilized man harbouring all kinds of vanity busies himself everywhere and has to calculate losses and gains everywhere. How can I not feel ashamed before you? Not only my mind but also my words fail to understand nature. Moreover, even if I have something to say, I cannot express it; even if I have some thoughts, I cannot let you understand. The mere bit of spirit inside is as though it were built into a stone wall that no light can pierce. Looking at you only with my eyes, how can I convey my meaning to you? What do I have to say who have forgotten my original language?

My young friends, however, pressed me to come and lie (it is lying when you try to say something when you have nothing to say). Knowledge, I cannot give you. If you want knowledge, of which I have none, you have to go to educators. Wisdom, of which I have less, is the flower and fruit in Hell. He who can get into and out of Hell will find some wisdom and who can't, none – I myself don't have any.

When I felt embarrassed, there came a saviour – the small picture in my hand – let me explain to you what I mean. This picture is a New Year card a friend made me. Look at this little kid who is playing by himself on the beach, feet in straw shoes, in one hand a flower which he tries hard to plant in the sands, and in the other a sprinkling can dripping water drop by drop. Not far from the kid are visible the rolling waves of the sea.

Have you seen what the picture means?

Planting a flower in the sands. Planting a flower in the sands! The little kid's enthusiasm for growing a flower will probably be in vain. Sands cannot support a fresh flower, neither can the few drops of fresh water help. Maybe the little flower would have given up its limited life withering away under the pressure of the sun before the kid could turn around. Moreover, the tidal waves are coming soon. When they come, even big-root trees cannot stand, let alone the small flower – so the flower on the beach is hopeless and the kid's effort definitely in vain.

You must be able to understand such a meaning.

My friend is very smart. He uses this picture to characterize us as a group of fools who take delight in daydreaming and who are eager to grow flowers on the sandy beach. The kid in the picture intends to maintain the flower's life with a few drops of fresh water, and we dreamers, too, want to sow a few seeds of art and thought with our most limited strength in the present society that is drier and more lifeless than the desert. Isn't it equally desperate, equally foolish? To plant a flower in the sands, to plant a flower in the sands, how ridiculous! But my smart friend said that the small picture meant more than that, and that sarcasm was not its end. It requires us to see more deeply. To us, it is stupid to plant a flower in the sands, but the kid himself is not aware of it. His thought is simple, and his belief, too. What does he know? What he knows is that the flower is lovely and that he should help the lovely thing grow. Usually he sees flowers and grass growing out of the ground and to him the sands on the beach are ground too. Why flowers cannot grow in the sands he does not consider, and he need not consider. What he knows is just to plant the flower and water it. As long as the flower stands upright, he will be delighted, jumping and singing, to praise the beautiful life. What will happen later to the sands and the flower he does no care at all. We know how children worship nature. Although his body is small, his soul is big; his clothes may be dirty, but his mind is clean. Here is another picture. It is about nature worship. Look at the child kneeling in the moonlight to worship a drooping lily. At that time her mind is as pure as the moonlight, as pretty as the flower and as quiet as the night. We may know that the kid planting a flower on the beach and the child worshiping one in the moonlight will kneel down, their thoughts

simple and pure; we may imagine that the former having planted the flower also worships and prays to it – having planted the flower for the moment is a success for him. After that, none of his business.

You see, this symbol is not only beautiful but also powerful, because it tells us that simple faith is the source of creation – the simple and pure innocence is the most powerful and everlasting thing the sun cannot scorch, the storm cannot break, the tide cannot wash away and darkness cannot cover up – flowers on earth may be destroyed and terminated sometime, but the "truth" that children love and plant flowers has an everlasting life.

Let's see a little bit further. The cultures we have now are nothing but human efforts and sacrifices in history. Why would people make efforts and sacrifices? Because they have natural faith. Their souls know what truth, goodness and beauty are, though their bodies and intellects sometimes may tempt them to go the other way. As long as they realize something is of eternal value, they will naturally become excited and automatically sacrifice themselves in order to redeem some evidence of eternal principles from the changing physical world. Why was Jesus not afraid of being crucified? Why would the blind Milton make poetry? Why would the deaf Beethoven compose music? Why would Michelangelo endure several months of damp regardless of his skin sticking to his boots in order to concentrate his attention on solving a small problem of fine art? Why are there always people going to explore the end of the Arctic Ocean and the summits of snowy mountains? Why would scientists spend their life span studying under the microscope or among numbers the theory that ordinary people can neither see nor understand.

It is because those humanist heroes all have their unshakable faith. Like our kid planting a flower in the sands, they have simple thought – religious people sacrifice themselves for principles of goodness, scientists for those of truth and artists for those of beauty – the results of all those sacrifices are our limited existent cultures.

Just think, isn't it equally foolish to do things on the ground, since like the sands the ground will not allow you to root in either and things here are as fragile as flowers? Just as the tide can wash away, the storm can break and the sun can scorch the flower that our kid is planting in the sands, so it is possible that all of our cultures will be washed away, broken and scorched at any time, isn't it? Where is the Babylonian civilization now? Pompeii has been buried under the ground for hundreds of years, and the Cretan civilization has not been fully discovered until recent fifty or sixty years. Moreover, sometimes the existence of an object cannot prove that its life still continues. There are ten million possibilities for the destruction of the mere globe itself. It is right for men to fear death. We fear the dead, but the most fearful are not the dead dead but the living dead. Nothing is more miserable than an existing body without a living soul. As for cultures, there are similar cases. Dead cultures are dead as it is, but the most pitiable are those half-dead ones struggling to breathe. If you ask me for an example, I will not hesitate to answer you, friends, the culture of your nation is a living dead one short of breath! It has been long since our last few forefathers sacrificed their breath and blood for the unchanging principles, gave up their limited existence for the undying life

Xu Zhimo

and encountered their contemporaries' mockery
and insults for the simple faith. It has been a long
time since we last heard the universal sound filling
the earth like tidal waters. It has been a long time
since we last saw the strong light sweeping across
the ground like a comet. It has been a long time
since we last shed hot blood for some ism. It has
been a long time since we had fortitude in our
marrow bones and weight in our words. That is
the saddest reflection. I really do not know what
an unpardonable offence this age has committed
that God should relentlessly give us such a
monstrous punishment. Just look around and see
where to find a whole man or a whole woman
nowadays – just look, nowadays which man is not
impotent and which woman not tympanitic.[①] In
order to describe our present suffering, we have
to coin a word uglier than ugliness, dirtier than
dirtiness, ignobler than ignobleness, cowardlier
than cowardice! Friends, really I often fear, fear
that the east wind will bring back next time not
the spring we are expecting, nor fresh flowers,

---

① Tympanitic: a medical term for the main symptom of schistosomiasis
or snail fever caused by schistosome or blood fluke, a kind of parasitic
flatworm swarming in rice fields. Chinese farmhands including women
used to get infected while working in the fields and many of them died.

64

green grass, butterflies and birds, but a dead season drier, sadder and lonelier than winter – for an ugly face does not go with pretty clothes. How are such ugly and abnormal humanity and society as ours entitled to ask the sky for sunlight, the earth for grass, birds for music and flowers for colours? If you ask me whether it will be fine or not tomorrow, I will reply that I do not know, or that perhaps not.

In the final analysis, we have lost the heart of our spiritual effort, that is, a simple belief, a pure innocence. Probably you are reluctant to take the trouble to plant flowers even in your own courtyard, let alone on the beach – who of us smart fellows would be a fool? The most terrible ghost of doubt and shadow of world-weariness have possessed our souls.

Therefore, friends, you who are youths and flowers bursting into bloom as the spring thunder has not stopped should not degenerate any more – although the trap opens its mouth wide before you, don't panic. Let your pure innocence fall down to fill it up and then move on – you must keep that bit of faith from which energy and courage and inspiration spring – fear being a fool no more. Try your best

Xu Zhimo

to plant flowers on the beach of humanity – the flowers may die, but their spirit will not decay.

1926

IDLE CHATTER ABOUT SOJOURNING IN FLORENTINE HILLS

Going out for a walk here, uphill or downhill, on a fine May evening is just like having a feast of beauty. Going to an orchard, for example, where every tree is burdened with the fruits of the most beautiful poetry, you may pick some just by raising your hand and taste the fresh flavour that is strong enough to make your soul drunk, if you are not satisfied just standing and looking. The sunlight is lukewarm, never too warm. The breeze is gentle and often comes through the blooming forest with a faint sweet smell and a breath of moist air to rub your face and wrap your shoulder and waist. Simply breathing is an immense pleasure. The atmosphere is always transparent, and with no mist in the near vales and no fog on the far peaks, the whole beautiful landscape just like a picture displayed before your eyes for leisurely appreciation.

The pleasure of sojourning in the hills especially

Xu Zhimo

lies in the fact that you need never hesitate over your dress or attitude. You may as well sway your grass-like disheveled hair, and tolerate the moss-like beard on your unshaven cheeks. You wear anything you like, dressing up as a shepherd, or a fisherman, or a farmhand, or a wandering gypsy, or a huntsman. You need no longer be anxious about your tie but may well go without it, to free your neck and chest for half or a day. You may wrap around your head a long gaudy scarf produced locally to imitate an officer of the Taiping Army,[1] or Lord Byron in his Egyptian attire. The most important thing, however, is to put on your most worn-out old shoes regardless of their bad appearance. They are your dearest friends, who bear your weight without letting you remember there are an extra pair of feet under your soles.

It is best to have such fun without company. I even want to prescribe strictly that you must be alone, because companions distract more or less, especially young females, who are the most dangerous and tyrannous travelling companions

---

[1] The army of the Taiping Heavenly Kingdom (1851-1864), established during the Taiping Rebellion, an uprising against the Qing dynasty in China. Its soldiers wore red scarves around their heads.

and whom you should shun like pretty snakes in the grass. Usually we go from our own home to a friend's, or to our workplace. That is nothing but moving from one cell to another within the same prison, where bondage always follows us and freedom never finds us. But if you have a chance to loiter alone in the beautiful hills or country between spring and summer, that is the time when you are really fortunate, and when you practically receive and personally taste freedom, and when your body and soul act in unison. That we have grown another year older, friends, merely means that we have added more weight to the yoke on our shoulder and tightened more the shackles around our ankles. Have we not ever admired children playfully rolling in the grass or sands or shallows, or kittens chasing their own tails? But our yoke and shackles are always our bosses who restrict our actions. Therefore, only when you alone by yourself run into nature's arms, like a naked child into its mother's, will you learn what the soul's pleasure is like, and what the happiness of simply living is like, and what the bliss of merely breathing or walking or looking or listening is like. So you have to be strictly self-serving, extremely selfish, that you only allow yourself, body and soul, to throb with the same pulse, undulate to the same sound waves, and enjoy yourself in the same miraculous universe as nature does. Our natural innocence is coy like the sensitive plant that coils up when touched by its fellows, but that lives uninhibitedly with natural movements in the clear sunlight and gentle breeze.

While you wandering alone, you may sit down or lie back, sometimes even roll, in the green grass, because the warm colour of the grass naturally awakes your childish liveliness; you may wildly dance an involuntary dance on a secluded path, looking at your own shadow changing into various weird shapes, because the shadows of the trees by the roadside indicate to you the pleasure of dancing with their slow movements; you may casually sing some fragmentary tune remembered by chance, or your own impromptu, because the orioles and swallows in the woods tell you that spring deserves praise; needless to say, your mind may naturally open and broaden with the stretching of the hill path; your heart may stay calm with the sight of the blue sky; your thought may join in singing with the

Xu Zhimo

waters in the valleys, which, sometimes transparent down to the bottom, sometimes ruffled and crumpled, run, run, run into the cool grove of olive trees, and the charming Arno...

Moreover, not only do you not need a companion whenever going on such an expedition, but also you do not have to bring a book with you. Although books are ideal companions, you should bring one aboard the train or in the living room of your dwelling place, but not as you walk about alone. What source of great, profound, exciting, clear, beautiful ideas cannot be found in the winds, clouds, rise and fall of the hills, colours and smells of the flowers? Nature is the greatest book, Goethe said, in every page of which we read sentences of the profoundest messages. And the words in the book are understood by everyone. The Alps and the Five-Elder Peaks,① Sicily and Mount Putuo,② the Rhine and the Yangtze, Lake Léman and the West Lake,③ Fujianese orchids④ and Chinese wayfaring trees, the snow-like reed catkins at the

---

① There are three mountains named the Five-Elder Peaks in China. The most famous one is located in Yongji County, Shanxi Province.
② Mount Putuo is a small island among the Zhoushan Islands off the east coast of China, famous for its Buddhist buildings.
③ There are a score of lakes by the name of West Lake in China. The most famous one is in Hangzhou City, Zhejiang Province.
④ Orchidaceae, a plant named for its major growing area, Fujian Province, is a traditional symbol of gentility in China.

West Stream, Hangzhou and the red tide at sunset, Venice, skylarks and nightingales, needless to mention the equally yellow wheat, equally purple wisteria, and equally green grass that grow on the same earth and wave in the same breeze – they all use the permanently consistent symbols, whose meanings are always clear. Unless you are blind and deaf, with your mind scarred, you are always entitled to the formless highest education and always enjoy the dearest free tonic. Only if you know this book, in the world you will not be lonely when being lonely, nor poor when being poor, comforted when being sorrowful, encouraged when being frustrated, urged when being cowardly, guided when being lost.

July 1925

Xu Zhimo

CAMBRIDGE AS I KNOW IT

1

There are emotional traces in most of my ups and downs. Not dwelling on other things, let me just talk about pursuing my studies. I came to the U.K. for Russell.[1] When he came to China, I had already been in the U.S. I did not shed enough tears when the untrue news of his death arrived but wrote an elegy. Of course I was glad he had not died. Having avoided the temptation to read for a doctorate at Columbia University, I crossed the Atlantic by ship intending to read some books seriously with the twentieth-century Voltaire, but when I arrived in the U.K., things had changed: Russell had been dismissed from Cambridge because of his pacifism during wartime and his

---

[1] Bertrand Russell (1872-1970), British philosopher and mathematician, visited China in 1921.

divorce; his fellowship at Trinity College was also taken away. Back from China he lived in London and earned a living with his wife by writing for periodicals. So I failed to realize my original wish to study with him. Having muddled along at the London School of Economics and Political Science for half a year, I got bored and was considering a change of course when I got to know Mr. Dickinson. Goldsworthy Lowes Dickinson was a well-known author. His two pamphlets *Letters from John Chinaman* and *A Modern Symposium* had won my admiration long before. I met him for the first time at a meeting of the League of Nations Union in London. On that day Mr. Lin Zong-meng[1] was delivering a speech at a meeting chaired by him. The second time was at Zong-meng's place, where we had tea together. Thereafter I went to his place frequently. He noticed my boredom and persuaded me to go to Cambridge, being himself a fellow at King's College. So I wrote to a couple of colleges to ask, but received the same reply: the enrolment quota had already been filled. Finally Mr. Dickinson

---

[1] Lin Zong-meng (1876-1925), alias Lin Chang-min, Chinese politician and man of letters, visited London in 1920-21.

succeeded in negotiating an agreement with his college to give me the status of a special student allowed to audit any course at will. From then on I also began to enjoy the advantages of wearing a black gown and mortarboard. At first I rented some small rooms at Sawston in the country six miles from Cambridge, living with my ex-wife Ms. Zhang You-yi and Mr. Guo Yu-chang.[1] Every morning I went to college by street car (sometimes by bike) and came back in the evening. I led such a life for a season but was still a stranger in Cambridge, knowing nobody. It can be said that I had not tasted the life in Cambridge at all. What I knew was a library, several classrooms, and two or three cafés for cheap food. Usually Dickinson was in London or the Continent, so I did not see him often. That autumn I returned to Cambridge alone[2] and in a whole year thereafter I gradually had chances to approach the genuine Cambridge life, and meanwhile "discovered" Cambridge proper. I had not known greater pleasure.

---

[1] Guo Yu-Chang (?-?), Chinese man of letters, was once the editor-in-chief of *Xue Deng (Study Light)*, the literary supplement to *Shi Shi Xin Bao (New Daily of Current Affairs)*.
[2] The author had divorced his wife then.

2

"Singleness" is a meaningful phenomenon. Sometimes I think it the first condition for any discovery. If you want to discover your friend's "sincerity," you have to have a chance to stay alone with him. If you want to discover your own sincerity, you have to give yourself a chance to be alone. If you want to discover a place (it has a living soul as well), you have to get a chance to enjoy yourself alone there. In our life, seriously speaking, how many people can we know? How many places can we know? We are all too busy to be alone. To be honest, I have even known little of my own home town. Cambridge is counted as one I know best, and the second may be only Florence, which I have got to know recently. Ah, those mornings, those evenings, I, alone, as if in a trance, in Cambridge! Absolutely alone.

But what a difficult work it is for one to write about his dearest one, no matter whether it is a person or a place. You are afraid, afraid of describing her badly, afraid of annoying her with overstatement, afraid of letting her down with

Xu Zhimo

understatement. Now I consider writing about Cambridge in such a state of mind. Having not tried before, I know I will not manage it this time – let alone a forced improvisation. Nevertheless, I have to write, the advertisement being out in the last issue. I think to write roughly in two parts: one about the natural scenery of Cambridge, and the other about student life in Cambridge. I can only do so much tonight, most briefly, and will supplement something later when I have an inspiration.

3

The soul of Cambridge lies in a river, the Cam, which, I dare say, is the most beautiful flow of water in the world. The river is named Granta, also called River Cam, and perhaps there is a difference between upper and lower reaches, about which I am not very clear. There are many curves in the river. In the upper reaches there is the famous Byron's Pool, where Lord Byron used to play. There is an old village called Granchester, where there is an orchard, where you can lie in the shade of luxuriant peach and plum trees having tea, when flowers or fruits may drop into your teacup, and little birds come to peck at the food on your table. That is really wonderful. Those are the upper reaches. Down from Chesterton are the lower reaches, where the river broadens and where boat races are held during spring and summer. There is a dam as the dividing line of upper and lower reaches, where the flow of water is very fast and where listening to the sounds of water in the starlight, of bells in the nearby village, or of tired cows chewing their cud on the river bank was one of my most mysterious experiences in Cambridge: nature's beauty, serenity, and harmony overwhelmed your soul unexpectedly in the conspiracy of the starlight and the waves.

The best parts of River Cam, however, lie in its middle reaches, the famous "Backs," where the buildings of several best known colleges sit on the banks. Down from the upper reaches are Pembroke, St. Catharine's, King's, Clare, Trinity, and St. John's. The most charming place is the boundary of Clare and King's College, the beauty of Clare adjacent to the sublimity of King's Chapel. Although in other places there might be more

Xu Zhimo

beautiful and sublime buildings, such as the regions around the Louvre on the Seine in Paris, the two ends of the Rialto Bridge in Venice, and the Ponte Vecchio in Florence, the Backs of River Cam have their own unique features, which cannot be easily described with one or two adjectives, and their unearth beauty goes beyond the scope of painting into the reach of music. There are not more symmetrical and harmonious buildings than that group. Among paintings, only Corot's fields might be comparable, and among music, Chopin's serenades. Even so, you will not get a clear impression of them, whose beauty is simply holy.

If you stand in the shade of the big beech tree by the bridge of King's College looking around, on your right, across a large square meadow, there is our fellows' building, which, though not very old, has unconcealable charm, its pale walls decorated with bright coloured roses shaking in the breeze during spring and summer, and, a bit to the left, the chapel, its forest-like unblemished steeples pointing to the sky forever, and, more to the left, Clare, oh, the incredibly delicate square court! Who can say this is not St. Clare's incarnation, and which stone does not shine with her holy spirit? Behind Clare vaguely visible is Trinity, the most luxurious and extravagant college in Cambridge, in its library on the river banks sitting the amazing statue of Lord Byron.

Your attention, however, is now magically caught by the triple-arched Clare Bridge. You have seen the Xiling Broken Bridge on the Bo Embankment of the West Lake, haven't you (it is a pity that it has been removed by the auto company representing the modern spirit of ugliness, and that it has now bid farewell to the world together with the desolate Leifeng Tower)? You cannot forget the bridge mottled with green mosses, lined with ancient fences, and framing with its arch the landscape of the lake and mountains, can you? Clare does not have such decent contrast. Neither is it comparable to the Guanyin Bridge by the Qixian Monastery on Mount Lu,[1] facing the wonderful Five-Elders Peaks above and the deep pond and flying waterfall below. It is a mere timid small bridge with triple arches, under which

---

[1] Mount Lu is located in Jiangxi Province, China, famous for its scenery and cultural heritage.

are mere glittering thin wavelets and dancing shadows of trees. Its small aligned railings topped by white marble balls at regular intervals are but the understated accessories like fragrant herbs and wild flowers in a village girl's hair. Nevertheless, gaze at it attentively, more attentively, reflect on your state of mind, and see if there remains any trace of worldly concerns. Only if your instinct for beauty has not died, this is a chance for you to realize the wonder of pure aesthetic experience.

But you have to choose the time for appreciation. Britain has extreme climate and weather. Winter is absurdly bad, when coming on continuous foggy days you must be willing without hesitation to go to Hell itself to have a try. Spring (Britain almost does not have summer) is even more absurdly lovely, especially its most mild and beautiful evenings in April and May are more precious than gold. An evening by the River Cam is a tonic for your soul. Oh, my sweet singleness then, my sweet leisure then. Evening after evening, I was seen leaning ecstatically on the bridge railings gazing into the western sky –

Looking at the still shadow of the bridge,
Counting the spiral ripples,
I warmed the moss on the stone railings,
And the moss cooled my nipples....

And a few more awkward lines – how can they describe the scene as subtle as gossamer?

Unforgettable evenings of July, far trees stiff still,
Like ink-painted hills, against the soft twilight,
Dense and thick, seven parts yellow, three parts green,
The subtle hint can only be caught on the border of autumnal dream....

4

Alongside the river there are all evergreen lawns. Looked out an upstairs window of the fellows' building, in the meadow on the opposite bank, no matter the time, morning or evening, there are always a dozen of yellow cows and white horses, with hooves up to ankles sinking in the wildly grown grass, grazing leisurely, tiny spots of yellow flowers shaking in the breeze in response to their tails' sweeps. The ends of the bridge are

Xu Zhimo

covered by leaning willows and beeches. The water is so clear that you can see down to the bottom of the river, less than four feet deep, carpeted evenly with long waterweeds. The lawn by the riverside is my favourite, on which, the natural carpet, in the morning and evening, I used to sit, sometimes reading, sometimes viewing the water, or lie, sometimes face up to gaze at the floating clouds in the sky, sometimes face down to embrace the warmth and softness of the earth.

Besides the loveliness on the banks, there is more fun on the river. You have to hire a boat to play. There is more than one kind: the ordinary boat with double oars, the light canoe, and the most particular punt. The last one is not often seen elsewhere: about six metres long, three feet wide, and you stand on the stern using a long pole to move it. I am all thumbs and have never succeeded in learning the skill. On your first try, you are likely to station your punt across the river, barging about awkwardly. The British might not easily laugh at others, but be careful of their silent frown! Who knows how many times the leisurely order on the river was broken by such a crude layman as me. I

Xu Zhimo

really have never learned successfully how to punt. Every time I went to hire a put to try again without admitting defeat, a white-bearded boatman used to say mockingly to me, "Sir, it's tiring to punt in the heat of the day. How about a canoe?" Heedless of his advice, I punted away with a single stroke of the pole, resulting in cutting the river into slices again.

Stand on a bridge and watch how easily and gracefully others punt. Especially on Sundays, there were several girl experts in white skirts, whose lower edges waved in the breeze, and in broad brimmed gauze hats, whose shadows shivered among the waterweeds. Look at their movements as they punted through the arches of the bridges: lifting a pole that seemed to have no weight, lightly, carelessly poking it into the centre of a ripple, squatting slightly, and the punt gliding forward like a fish with a splash out of the shade of the bridge. Their swiftness, leisureliness, and lightness are really praiseworthy.

As the early summer sun was getting warmer, you might hire a small boat, and row into the shade by a bridge to read or dream, with fragrant locust tree flowers floating on the surface of the water, and the feeding noise of a school of fish around your ears, or in the early autumn evening, in the cold light of the crescent moon, far into some hidden place in the upper reaches. Revel-loving youths with their girlfriends, having Japanese paper lanterns set up in pairs on the gunwales and soft mats spread on the decks, bringing radios with them, also rowed towards deserted places to enjoy their country pleasures – who would not like to hear the music played under the surface of the water on the serene river describing dreams and springtime?

Those who are used to city life do not easily know the changes of the seasons. They know that it is fall on seeing the leaves fall, and that spring, green; they set up a stove when it is cold, and take it apart when it is hot; they take off padded robes to put on lined ones, and take off lined ones to put on unlined ones. That's all. All the tidings of the stars overhead, soil underfoot, and breaths of air do not concern us. Busy with so many things like this and like that, who cares about the movement of the stars, growth and death of grass and flowers, and the changes of winds and clouds? At the same time we complain about the pain, sorrow, restriction, and dullness of our life. Who would admit that it is happy to be human? Who would not curse life more or less?

Unsatisfactory life, however, is mostly asked for by yourself. A believer in life, I believe that life is by no means so dark as what most people learn merely from their own experiences. The root cause of our trouble lies in "forgetting." Humankind is so much a child of nature as flowers and birds. Only unfortunately we are civilized, the more grown up, the further from nature. How can they be happy and alive, the flowers without soil, the fish without water? From nature, we got our life; from nature, we should get our follow-up nourishment. Which big thriving tree does not have twisted roots deep inside the earth? We are never independent. Happy are the children who never depart from their mother, and healthy the people always close to nature. To cure us of our present dull life, there is no need for camping with deer and boars, or returning to caves, but "forgetting not nature completely," a casual prescription that is enough, hopefully, to relieve our symptoms. Having a few rolls in the grass, a few baths in the sea, and a few looks from a height at sunrise and sunset – you will have the burden on your shoulders lightened.

That is the shallowest of reasoning, of course. Nonetheless I would not be so sure of myself if I had not spent days in Cambridge. Only that spring in my life, it is pitiable to say, was not spent in vain. Only during that spring, my life is natural, and really pleasant (though it happened to be the time when I suffered most from life). I have plenty of leisure, plenty of freedom, and plenty of absolute solitude then. Strangely, I seemed for the first time to have recognized the brightness of the moon and stars, the greenness of grass, the sweetness of flowers, and the hospitality of flowing waters. How can I forget the glances of the early spring? On many mornings, by myself, I braved the cold to walk in the frosted glade – to hear birds sing, to wait for sunrise, to seek for flowers waking gradually in the soil, to experience the subtlest and most miraculous message of spring. Oh, there is the newly coming thrush practicing its new song on the incompletely bare green branch. Oh, here is the first edelweiss bloom struggling out of the

Xu Zhimo

half-frozen ground. Oh, isn't the newly arriving moisture sticking to the lonely willow?

So quiet, on the wet main road in the morning, only the bell of a milk-delivery van in the distance disturbs the silence around. Down the road, until the end, turn off and onto a path among the woods, go deep into the misty inside, where dim twilight leaks down from the intervals between the intertwining elm branches overhead. Go farther ahead, out of the woods, in front of level fields, where there are cottages in sight, wheat fields just turning green, and two or three small bread-shaped hills hiding a path farther away. On the misty horizon, the pointed shadow is the steeple of a nearby village chapel. Listen, the slow and clear sound of the morning bells. This region is the central plain of the country, topographically like the mild waves on the sea, silently moving up and down. Mountains are not visible but evergreen grasslands and rich fields. Mount that mound and look – Cambridge is merely a stripe of dense forest clustering around a few graceful steeples. The charming River Cam is out of sight too. You can only imagine the flow of the clear water among the flourishing trees. Cottages and woods are the pieces on this checkerboard. Where there is a village, there is good shade, and vice versa. Morning is the time to view cooking smoke: the mist rising gradually, the grey veil of the heavens lifted (best after a light shower of soft hail), cooking smoke here and there, in strands, in skeins, in curls, light, heavy, dark grey, light blue, pale, gradually going up in the still atmosphere and then disappearing, like people's morning prayers reaching the gate of heaven one after another. The morning sun is seldom seen in early spring. It will be the greatest delight to early birds when it does appear. In a instant the fields are touched with more colour, and the grass, trees, paths, cottages, all covered by a golden veil. In a instant the glamorous softness of the morning overflows all about. In a instant your heart shares the glory of the birth of the day. "Spring!" the victorious clear sky seems to whisper in your ear. "Spring!" your delighted soul seems to echo back there.

Keep an eye out for the scene on the river, because it is different every day since the coming of spring. Take care about the mosses on the

Xu Zhimo

stones, the fresh flowers among the decayed grass, the speed of the water flow, the growth of the waterweeds, the coloured clouds in the sky, the newly made birdsongs. The timid edelweiss is the messenger boy of spring. The lilies-of-the-valley and sweet herbs are the first heralds of joy. The pretty primroses, the delicate daffodils, the revel-loving crocuses, the hardship-enduring dandelions and daisies – now spring is already everywhere in the world, needless to fish for its information frequently any longer.

The splendid blooming of spring. This is the time for you to roam around. Lovely road. Unlike in China, where is there not a wide and smooth road here? Hiking is a pleasure, but biking a greater one. In Cambridge biking is a common technique: women, children, and old men all enjoy the pleasure of the double-wheel dance. (It is said that bicycle theft is not a worry in Cambridge, because everyone has his own and no one steals.) Choose any direction as you will, take any road you please, and bike down with the gentle grass-scented breeze, half a day's leisure will surely be a tonic for your soul. There is plenty of cooling shade and good grass along the road for you to rest in anywhere. If you love flowers, there are a lot of gorgeous meadows here. If you love birds, there are a lot of sweet-tongued songbirds here. If you love children, there are lovable kids everywhere in the countryside. If you love people, there are many country folk who do not dislike visitors here, and you may put up for the night everywhere with milk and potato for supper and colourful fruits for dessert. If you love drink, there are best fresh brews for you in every country pub here, and stout being too strong, cider and ginger beer may serve to quench your thirst. ...Bring a book with you, bike ten miles, select a quiet place to gaze into

Xu Zhimo

the sky, listen to the birds and read the book, and then tired, lie down in the deep grass to seek for a dream – can you imagine a more healthy and enjoyable pastime?

Lu You[①] wrote the couplet, "Although having the fast horse called to meet the new moon, / I mounted the light sedan chair to enjoy the evening cool." That is a local official's style. Although there are neither horse nor sedan chair for me in Cambridge, I have my style: I used to bike at sunset after the big disc of the sun above the horizon. The sun could not be caught up, of course. I was not as crazy as Kua Fu,[②] but I enjoyed secretly much of the lovely evening scenery in that way. A few experiences like vivid pictures still remain now. Just to mention the sunset, usually we only know to view it from mountaintops or the seaside, but in fact the sunset viewed from plains is just as wonderful sometimes, as long as it is against a big sky. Once I went to a place, with my hands on the fence of a cottage, across a field of wheat, to view the changes of the western sky. At another time,

---

① Lu You (1125-1210), flourishing in Song dynasty, is probably the most prolific Chinese poet. The quoted lines are from his poem "Drunk, Touring to the White Cliff and then Back".
② Kua Fu, a hero of Chinese myth, raced against the sun and died of thirst as he caught up with it.

just facing a wide road on which there came a flock of sheep back from grazing, with such a big sun behind them radiating ten thousand golden rays, feeling inside at once some mystical pressure at the sight of the road and the flock of living creatures in the blinding light against the dark blue sky, I did kneel down, in front of the fading golden light. Still, at another time, there was a more unforgettable scene: an endless meadow with bright red poppy blooms, which, like ten thousand golden lanterns standing outstandingly in the green grass, shone on by the sun aslant through cracks between the brown clouds, turned into something mysteriously purple, transparent, blinding, in a instant in my dazzled vision, changed into... Oh, forget it. You won't believe it.

It is more than two years since I have departed from you, Cambridge. Who knows my homesick pangs? I want nothing else but the curfew-shaken evenings, the fenceless fields, and leaning alone in the soft grass, to see the first big star appear on the edge of the sky.

15 January 1926

Xu Zhimo

THE UGLY WEST LAKE

"I'd like to compare the West Lake to the West Lady, / Whom heavy or light make-up always fits perfectly."[1] We have idealized the West Lake too much. Summer is the time when the West Lake puts on heavy make-up. The willow trees along the embankment are all dark green, and the lotus leaves and flowers around the inner part of the lake all flourishing. Which is not a ready-made poetic subject matter, the morning mist, or the evening clouds? But do you love this West Lady? I don't. This time I turned and ran away as soon as I saw her. What is West Lake but a pot of stinking warm broth! The lake is shallow and the water does not flow. In addition, the lake is recently full of big fish, some of them even so big as to weighing more than fifty pounds, which have destroyed all the

---

[1] A couplet from Su Shi's (1037-1101) poem "Drinking on the Lake When It Rained after Being Fine". The West Lake here refers to the one located in Hangzhou City, Zhejiang Province, the best-known of several namesakes in China. The West Lady is a famous beauty flourishing during the Spring and Autumn Period (770-476) in Chinese history, comparable to Helen of Troy in the West.

graceful waterweeds. The water is turbid, and, what's more, the fishy smell most unbearable. As to the fish breeding in the lake, I have heard many kinds of explanation and do not know which is true: some said that it was simply a way the government made profit, and that, with such a big fish pond, wasn't it easy to breed fish and sell them when they grew up? Some said breeding fish was to prevent the overgrowth of waterweeds lest they overfill the lake, and some said that those big fish were bought from other places by some big philanthropists to set free in the lake for the purpose of pursuing the goal of longevity or offspring or profits, and that fishing nowadays not allowed by the authorities. Anyway, the West Lake has become a fish pond indeed. It is said that it has not rained a single drop in Hangzhou since June, resulting in the shrinkage of the lake, of course, like a beauty suffering from amenorrhoea, and the smell! It is not easy for us who are used to living in the North to believe how hot it is in the South this year. The heat never subsides all night through, let alone during the day. It is getting hotter and hotter with a blazing sun every day and bright stars every night. Hangzhou is more unbearable than Shanghai. Exposed to the burning sun, the shallow water in the West Lake gets not far from boiling within a few hours and will never cool down unless a gale blows, for the heat can only come but not go, what with hills all around the city. That day I did not hire a boat to tour the lake until the evening, thinking it cooler on the water than on the banks. Well, it was endurable without a wind, but unbearable with one, which, warm and smelly, made people feel dizzy and queasy. A friend of mine in the same boat fell ill at once. In my memory the desert winds alongside the Red Sea seem more endurable. By twelve o'clock midnight when we went home it was still quite hot. And the mosquitoes and gnats on the lake were simply flocks of big waterfowl. They served me right as soon as I was seated.

It is too hard for the West Lake, only the smell being unbearable enough. And among the places of interest around the lake, originally the most quiet and attractive one was "the Autumnal Moon over the Calm Lake," where, with a square terrace, a few willow trees, and a zigzag corridor, it was something special to sit viewing the lake on a cool moonlit night of autumn, and, what's more, you might always occupy the place, frequented by few people, alone during the night. It was really blessed to spend half a night chatting with several friends there, having woken up the keeper to make a bowl of tea or lotus root paste for each. Three years ago I went there with some friends good at zither and flute. It was really a rare refined pleasure to lie back under a poplar tree looking at the fragmentary moonlight and listening to the rolling music on the surface of the water. The West Lake has been being vulgarized at a tremendous pace. It hurts me once more to go there every time: the Leifeng Tower[1] gone because of embarrassment, the Broken Bridge turned into a highway bridge, Hardoon[2] having built a mansion in the centre of the lake, some rich young master's motorboat creating storms on the shallow water, smoke from factory chimneys having taken place of the mist around the hilltops, and the drums and gongs of the Big World or some other stages acting as the singing

---

[1] Leifeng Tower, a well-known Buddhist pagoda in Hangzhou City, Zhejiang Province, China, was built in 975, fallen down in 1924, and rebuilt in 2001.

[2] Silas Aaron Hardoon (1851-1937), British Jewish millionaire, born in Bagdad, flourished in Shanghai. He purchased through some improper means the piece of public land at the side of the scenic spot "the Autumnal Moon over the Calm Lake" of the West Lake district in 1918 and built a mansion with a large garden there.

birds instead on the lake. West Lake, West Lake, what else that you have is worthy of admiration? Don't you believe that "the Autumnal Moon over the Calm Lake" will be ruined this time?

"Boatman, let's go to 'the Autumnal Moon over the Calm Lake,' where it is quieter, anyway."

"'The Autumnal Moon over the Calm Lake?' Quieter, sir? No quieter. Now open pubs. Pubs real busy. Look, you see, people in white, so many, fanning themselves with fans so lively. And singing girls, too, all teenagers. Listen – it's a Wuxi folk song. Fiddlers all jolly good..."

Let's go to the Building beyond Buildings[①] then. Who knows the Building beyond Buildings will be another hurt! Originally the two-storied old house of the Building beyond Buildings diagonally faced the Pavilion in the Centre of the Lake, with several old tables as clean as a whistle, one or two old waiters, fresh fish and shrimps, slippery water shields, a pot of old rice wine, a plate of salted peanuts. I used to snatch a moment of leisure to enjoy alone the small

---

① The Building beyond Buildings is the name of a well-known restaurant in Hangzhou, which is derived from the lines from the poem "Written on the Wall of a Lin'an Inn" by the Song Dynasty poet Lin Sheng (fl. 1106-1170): "There are blue mountains beyond mountains and buildings beyond buildings, / And at what time will the singing and dancing on the West Lake come to an end?"

amount of antiquity there every time I went to
the West Lake. From the shade of willow trees
on the edge of the embankment, you leaning
against the rail got different views of the lake
in fine, rainy, and snowy weathers, or a more
appealing atmosphere when the moon climbed
over the tops of the willow trees. Its advantage lay
in quietness. Most time in the evening you might
occupy the whole dining hall on your own. It was
hard to describe the joy you felt, sipping at your
warm wine as chatting with the old waiter about
the lake views or market prices of fish and shrimps.
But now even the Building beyond Buildings has
changed! The location remains the same, but the
restaurant there has been rebuilt into a western-
style three-storied roofed building, dazzling with a
fresh coat of paint. The fast rotation of the electric
fans upstairs is visible even from the lake, diners
crowd there noisily, and waiters in western-style
tails were substituted for the old friends. All gone,
the leisure and interest. We can do nothing but
have a table moved to the roadside downstairs to
eat something. It turns out that even the starters
have changed. How sad. Tagore came to China

and sighed with huge disappointment. He said, "There is no other nation in the world like yours who deliberately creates the spirit of ugliness." No wonder the old man complained. What high (maybe a poet's) expectations of China he had as he came, but what kind of reality he saw! Mr. Dickinson wrote a wonderful essay about his impression after touring Mount Tai. He contrasted westerners' vulgarity and our elegance, their philistinism and our leisure spirit. He said that only the Chinese people knew how to love and preserve nature, and that the accessories they added to landscapes do not betray nature at all. Actually they always tried to supplement the beauty of nature, and would not allow landscapes spoiled. They built on mountains along the winding grain tracks, which, paved with local stone, are themselves full of interest. They would rather sacrifice some convenience than destroy the harmony of nature. So what they built was attractive paths, while the Europeans and Americans came to construct either roads or elevators through the mountains. They inscribed on natural rocks beautiful poems, painted green, which looked ancient and interesting among the mosses, in contrast to the European and American mountain rocks, on which only advertisements for cigars and various other products were visible. They made the red wall of a Buddhist monastery partly emerge from the dense forest, while the westerners erected multi-storied noisy hotels there. It is said that the Chinese ought to imitate the West, but I wonder who on earth should play the part of the modest student.

That is a paragraph of Mr. Dickinson's impression of China fifteen years ago. I wonder what other wonderful essay he would have written to eulogize our virtues if he had come back to see the achievements of the West Lake.

The West Lake is really an irony. With regard to the scenic beauty, it indeed has a place in the world. The colourful hills and waters are its particular attraction, engendering love in one compulsively. Unfortunately, however, the Hangzhou people (I myself am counted as one too) are somehow particularly vulgar and loathsome. The uneducated are lacking in taste, but the educated more detestable. Only their quack-quack accent of the local vernacular is annoying enough. Evidently the Hangzhou folks are not only good talkers (they really are!) but also good doers. With respect to "enterprises," there have been quite a lot of construction recently, such as all the six arched bridges linking the embankment bing straightened to serve the interests of the auto company, but unfortunately the design of landscape is another kind of enterprise, not running a shop, securing one's official position, that sort of thing. Usually we say that the owner has to have good taste in natural beauty even to arrange a small garden. Now the whole West Lake is in the hands of a group of big bosses. I dare not guess what they usually have in their minds, but judging from their achievements, theirs are indeed the kind of minds that solely aim at increasing the total income of "our Hangzhou" commercial circles. The shopkeepers may benefit more or less, but how about poor West Lake? Obviously a born beauty is forced to have a group of tough guys do her make-up for her. Even if there are not other embarrassing situations created, the act itself is sufficient to spoil our appetite. Alas, the sad West Lady!

But then again, nowadays who has time for

Xu Zhimo

beauty? So far the South has been counted as a paradise. In other areas, human lives just equal those of worms. You dare not go even if there is a way, and you dare not speak even if you have something to say. Why affect the stale pose of a gentleman and find fucking fault with something beautiful or not then?

7 July 1926

THE PLEASURE OF A SNOWFLAKE

Oh, If I were a small snowflake
Floating in air in a free state,
  I'd clearly see my way —
  Flying, flying, flying —
There, on the ground, is my way.

Not heading for the cold vale,
Nor the lonely foot of the hill,
  Nor deserted street astray —
  Flying, flying, flying —
You see, I have my own way!

Gliding gracefully in space,
Aiming at that peaceful place,
  Waiting for her to come —
  Flying, flying, flying —
Oh, she smells of plum bloom

THE PLEASURE OF A SNOWFLAKE

Then I would use my lightness
Lightly to stick on her dress,
  Close to her soft bosom —
  Melting, melting, melting —
Into her wavelike soft bosom.

30 December 1924

Xu Zhimo

SAYONARA
(For a Japanese Lady)

How tender is the drooping of the head,

  As coy as a water lily unable to bear the cold breeze.

Bid farewell, bid farewell —

  In the farewell there is a bittersweet —

  Sayonara![1]

[1] Sayonara, Japanese, means "farewell" or "goodbye". This is the last one of a sequence of eighteen poems written during May or July 1924.

110

A PALE SPARK

I sit alone on a stone halfway ,
   Watching the white clouds over the hill;
A little bird whose name I do not know
   Is mocking and laughing at my lost soul.

The white clouds rise up one by one
   High into the sky far and wide,
But here in my narrow heart, alas,
   Are gathering clouds sorrowful and sad!

The bright morning twilight is unveiled
   To wash the green-island-like hilltops;
A pale spark is burning in my bosom
   Like the faint will o' the wisp among tombs.

But the pale spark faint and weak
   Shines on the remains and embers;
Though a mockery of the past traces

Xu Zhimo

It lasts long through the course of the years.

1925

TO SEEK FOR A BRIGHT STAR

I rode on a blind and crippled horse
  Whipping it through the night —
  Whipping it through the night,
I rode on a blind and crippled horse!

I rushed into the long dark night
  To seek for a bright star —
  To seek for a bright star,

Xu Zhimo

I rushed onto the dark lone height.

Tired, tired the beast that I straddle,
    Yet the star is not out —
    Yet the star is not out,
Tired, tired the rider in the saddle.

Now a silvery light permeates the sky,
    On the height falls a horse,
    In the night lies a corpse —
Now a silvery light permeates the sky!

23 November 1924

A PICTURE OF THE LEIFENG TOWER UNDER THE MOON

I send you a shape of the Leifeng Tower
With a skyful of clouds black and white;
I send you a top of the Leifeng Tower,
On the sleeping waves a moon shedding light.

Dark dark night, slim slim tower,
Round round moon, smooth smooth stream —
If only we were rowing an uncovered boat,
If only we had created a perfect dream!

26 September 1923

Yu Zhima

RARE

Rare, so quiet the night,
   Rare, so warm the stove,
Even rarer, silent together,
   A pair of lonely souls!

No plot, no comment,
   Nor pretension, doubt or hate,
Only sitting silent by the fire,
   Counting the strokes far away.

Drink a mouthful of water, friend,
   To moisten your dry lips;
Put more coal on the fire, friend,
   To earn the gratitude of the flames.

In the icy winter night, friend,
   The hard-earned fuel is treasured;
In the icy cold world, a few
   Sympathetic hearts get together.

1925

COUNTRY SOUNDS

The boat drifts slowly in the shadow of the willow —
  A breath of cool breeze of early autumn
  Has creased the surface of the water,
The breath, has brought the country sounds along the flow.

Alone, I sit idly by the window of the boat,
  Quietly, looking at the ripples of the river,
  Quietly, listening to the sounds far and near —

Xu Zhimo

Again, childish delight in my memory afloat!

That is the clear shouting of young children,
*   In the fields, farm workers are busy*
*   By the fences, dogs and chickens noisy:*
But oh, the sad, sad feeling without reason!

White clouds drift high in the deep blue sky:
*   I would give my sorrowful years*
*   Together with my lovelorn tears*
All to the boundless void — let them pass by,

And return to my beautiful, childish innocence,
*   Like a well of cold spring in the vale,*
*   Like a young dove in the morning gale,*
Like a flower by the pond, of natural fragrance.

1925

BY THE MOUNTAIN ROAD

By the mountain road, on a misty morning,
A newborn blue bloom peeped out of the grass,
And I saw her off, parting with her there —
Her white skirt trailing across the green grass.

I 'd not spoken, and she'd not said goodbye,
Stopping by the mountain road, I meditated,
"Isn't it the best time to reveal your secret?" —
The dewy flower was impatient as I hesitated.

Why hesitate? This is the last chance,
By the mountain road, in the misty morning.
I gathered my strength and turned to her —
But why? Her eyes were full of mourning.

I swallowed my words and hung my head:
Fire and ice in my bosom fiercely roiled;
Ah, I've known my fate and her sorrow —

In the thick mist, by the lonely road!

That morning, by the misted mountain road,
The newborn blue bloom peeked out of the grass,
I saw her off, parting with her forever —
The white skirt trailing across the green grass.

1924

Xu Zhimo

NO. 7, STONE TIGER LANE[①]

Our small courtyard, sometimes, is brimful of boundless tenderness:

Giggling Lady Vine exposes her bosom to Persimmon Palms' caress,

Tall Elder Locust Tree bends down in the breeze to embrace Maid Crabapple,

The yellow dog by the fence, guards the sleeping baby Po, his little pal,

And the newly-made love song sung by the small bird, courting, sounds endless—

Our small courtyard, sometimes, is brimful of boundless tenderness.

Our small courtyard, sometimes, is painted with a faint dream view:

The dimness woven with green shades after rain forms a piece of fine silence,

A frog sitting on the withered orchid hears the earthworm singing next door,

A sheet of rain cloud before dissolving unrolls above the old locust tree,

What are those dancing in circles around the eaves, bats or dragonflies?

Our small courtyard, sometimes, is painted with a faint dream view.

Our small courtyard, sometimes, is slightly sighing with despair:

Despairing of the numerous red petals beaten by the violent shower,

---

① No. 7, Stone Tiger Lane, Xidan, Beijing was the Department of Foreign Language Books of the Peking Songpo Library, where the poet once worked as a librarian.

124

Despairing of the green leaves falling before drying in early autumn,

Despairing of the moon departing by the cloud-boat at midnight, already

Beyond the west wall, while an elegiac tune is blowing in the cold air —

Our small courtyard, sometimes, is slightly sighing with despair.

Our small courtyard, sometimes, is deeply dipped in happiness:

In the evening after rain, there are only shades, fragrance and breeze,

And the old lame drunk, big mug in hand, his crooked foot pointing at the sky,

Pint after pint, bottoms up, a heart full of joy, a face red with wine,

In the nonstop laughter, floating and drifting the drunk like an immortal —

Our small courtyard, sometimes, is deeply dipped in happiness.

July 1923

Xu Zhimo

A NIGHT IN FLORENCE

Surely you are going, tomorrow? Then I, I...

Never mind, sooner or later the day will come;

Remember me if you would, or quickly

Forget the fact that in the world there is

I, lest it annoys you when recalling me;

Take me merely as a dream, a fantasy,

Or the remaining petals we saw the other day

Shivering timidly in the wind, one,

Two, fallen down, trodden, turned into mud...

Alas, trodden, turned into mud — that's all,

So much better than being half-dead like this,

Looked down on as pitiable and burdensome —

My goodness! For what, for what did you come...

I cannot forget you, who came to me that day,

Like a light on the dark untrodden way.

You are my teacher, my love, my savior;

You have taught me what life is, and what love,

Woken me up from my swoon and returned my innocence.

Xu Zhimo

Without you how can I know the sky so high

And the grass so green? Feel my heart, how fast it beats,

And my face, how badly it burns; thanks to the darkness,

They are not seen. Love, I can hardly breathe;

Kiss me no more. I can't bear the fire-like life.

Now my soul is like a bar of iron on the anvil

Under the hammer of love, battered, battered,

Sparks scattered everywhere... I'm fainting. Hold me,

Love, here in the quiet garden, eyes closed,

Just let me die on your bosom. How beautiful!

The wind among the poplars overhead, whistling,

Would be my elegy, the breeze coming through

The olive grove with the smell of pomegranate

Carry my soul away, and the fireflies, amorous

And attentive, light my way. I would not stop

Until arriving at the bridge with three arches,

Hearing you holding my luke-warm body here,

Sadly calling me, kissing me, shaking me, biting me...

And then I would go on with the fresh breeze,

Following it to heaven, to hell, to anywhere,

Anyway, to cast off the loathsome life, and realize

The death in love. Isn't dying in love better

Than being reborn five hundred times? ...Selfish,

I know, but I don't care... You'll die together with me?

What? Not to be a couple isn't perfect death-in-love.

To ascend must be wing to wing in pairs as well;

In heaven we'd look after each other all the same;

I could not do without you, nor could you without me.

Should it be hell, you'd worry more if I go there alone,

You said that hell was not necessarily less civilized

(Though I don't believe), but a tender flower like me

Couldn't be certainly free from being weather-beaten.

At that time when I called you, you'd not hear me —

Isn't it a fall into a muddy pit instead of liberation,

With the cold-eyed devils and the cold-hearted men

Laughing at my fate, and your cowardly carelessness?

It sounds reasonable, too. What shall I do then?

It's hard to live, too hard, and not free even if dead,

And I'll not let you sacrifice yourself for me...

Alas! You said it was better to wait, wait for that day!

Is there that day? — As long as you are here, I have faith,

But you have to go at daybreak. Can you really bear

To go without me? And I can't keep you, it's fate;

But this flower, without sunshine, without dewdrops,

Will wither even though not dying at once. How sad!

You can't forget me, love. Except in your heart,

I live nowhere. Yes, I obey you, I'll wait,

I've to wait patiently until the iron tree blossom.

Xu Zhimo

Love, you are a bright star over my head forever:

Should I die unfortunately, I'd change into a firefly,

In this garden, close to grass roots, flying darkly,

From dusk to midnight, from midnight to break of day.

If only there were no cloud in the sky, I could see

Up there above the changeless big star. That's you.

May you shed more light for me, through the night,

Across the sky, keeping on communing by love....

In the hills of Florence, 11 June 1925

HAPHAZARD

I am a fragment of cloud in the sky,

Casting a haphazard shadow among your waves —

  Please don't be surprised,

  Nor even pleased —

And in an instant shall vanish without a trace.

We meet on the nightly sea, you and I,

Xu Zhimo

You have yours, and I, my direction;

Good for you to memorize,

But best to forget

The lights of intercourse that mutually shone.

1926

LOOKING AT THE MOON

The moon, through the window gauze, in the dark,
I gaze at her struggling up the craggy mountain-shoulder,
A disc of drowsy and clumsy, messy and lazy gloss:
Like a virgin, holding her chastity tight,
Frightened, struggling out of the violent claws.

This reminds me of you, my love, once, too,
Having struggled between the fangs of misfortune.
But now, just like the bright moon in the blue space,
You've climbed up onto the front peak of good fortune,
Shedding light on the unevenness of the earth's face.

1926

GODLY HERO

This is a heap of rocks rough and ugly,

And that, a crowd of lilies bright and pretty;

But as the Moon paints the flowery shadow on the stony

Surface, the rough and ugly also become pretty.

Xu Zhimo

I am a lump of ordinary-looking mortal,
And hers, an immortal face, incomparable;
But as Love pushes her into my arms' circle,
Such a fellow as I also becomes a godly hero!

1927

THE VAST SEA

The vast sea or void sky I'd not like,

Or want to fly a huge kite

High up to tease the wind from each limit;

    I want only a minute,

    I want only a flash,

    I want only a crack —

  Like a child leaning over

  The windowsill of a dark room

  To watch in the western sky an undying

Crack, a

Flash, a

Minute.

1931

Xu Zhimo

VIEWING ABOARD

1

I have to praise the day
Of May towards its end;
Embracing clouds and trees
Are those neat rice fields.

2

The white clouds crossing the clear heavens
Are like the white swallows from fairy islands,
And their white feathers with the golden hem
As the evening twilight shines on them.

3

Carrying the light coolness of the evening,
Oxen, released from work, stand dreaming:
Children crouching beside, want to

Xu Zhimo

Climb onto their backs, cool, to be a hero!

4

In the dense shades of the trees,
A brook, and a white stone bridge;
Under the arch comes early the night,
And stars twinkle in the flowing water.

5

Green is the bean patch, shady the mulberry grove,
Luxuriant the grass by the stream,
Quiet the farmland scene in the evening,
But listen, the flying of the insects!

6

The moon puts on her make-up at dusk;
The sun flurriedly flees toward the horizon.
He's afraid of seeing her, and being seen by her —
She would laugh at his red face of a drunk!

1930

AGAIN, ADIEU TO CAMBRIDGE

Softly, softly I'm going away,
  As softly as I came here softly;
And softly raising a hand to wave
  Goodbye to the clouds in the west sky.

The golden willows by the riverside
  In the twilight are brides who look so smart;
Their shining shadows cast in the water
  Wavering and wavering in my heart.

The green hornwort on the soft mud
  Of the river bed sways long and sleek:
In the smooth streams of the River Cam
  I'd rather be a leaf of waterweed!

The pond in the shade of the elm
  Is a rainbow — not of the streams —
Scattered among the floating algae,
  Crystallizing iridescent dreams.

Xu Zhimo

To seek for dreams? Wield a long pole
*   Rowing into the greener reeds*
To carry a full load of starlight,
*   Singing aloud in the brilliant beams.*

But now I cannot sing aloud;
*   Quiet is the music for a parting rite.*
Summer insects silent for me, too,
*   So silent is Cambridge tonight!*

Softly, softly I am going away,
*   As softly as I came here softly;*
I have waved my sleeves and waved off
*   All the coloured clouds in the west sky.*

6 November 1928

CUCKOO

Cuckoo, the amorous bird, she's singing all through the night:
In the deep shade of summer, looking up at the floating clouds
Like flying moths encircling the bright light of the moon,
With starlight scattered as the fishing-lights on the shore,
And the sweet night-tide resting in the dense dew,
She sings. When she sings, "Cut the wheat 'n' sow the rice" —
Farmhands wake up with a start at the break of day.

The amorous cuckoo, she's chattering all through the night.
Is it complaint? Or admiration? Her heart's full of love
And bitterness that is transformed into a new song,
With a tender feeling trembling in the arms of the night;
She sings, her mouth dripping blood, spot after spot,
Dyeing red the dew-damp grass leaves, and morning light
Rocking lightly the dreams of the garden. She cries,
She cries, she cries out, "I love you, darling."

1929

Xu Zhimo

IN THE MOUNTAIN

The courtyard is quiet all around
   Surrounded by market noise;
Pine shadows weaved on the ground —
   Lo, the moon overhead!

Not knowing what a scene is there
   In the mountain tonight:
There must be the moon, pine trees,
   And a silence much deeper,

I want to cling to the moonlight,
   And be changed into a breeze,
To awaken the spring-drunk pines
   To drift among the peaks;

And to blow a green pine needle,
   Down to your windowsill,
As light and soft as a sigh —

Not to interrupt your sleep still.

1 April 1931

Xu Zhimo

"I DO NOT KNOW IN WHICH QUARTER THE WIND IS BLOWING"

I do not know

In which quarter the wind is blowing —

In a dream I am, oh,

To the dreamy wavelets going.

I do not know

In which quarter the wind is blowing —

In a dream I am, oh,

Her tenderness, my ecstasy flowing.

I do not know

In which quarter the wind is blowing —

In a dream I am, oh,

The sweetness, the dreamy glowing.

I do not know

In which quarter the wind is blowing —

In a dream I am, oh,

Her betrayal, my sorrowful knowing.

I do not know
In which quarter the wind is blowing —
In a dream I am, oh,
Heartbroken in the dream growing.

I do not know
In which quarter the wind is blowing —
In a dream I am, oh,
Faintness, the dreamy glowing.

1928

Xu Zhimo

IN SICKNESS

Fallen sick, I lie in bed listlessly, watching

The cloudy sky, hearing the leaves in the wind...

Is it bird-song? There is warm sunlight in the courtyard,

Withering grass all over the ground, creepers on the wall,

And clusters of crimson or grey leaves, shivering,

Turning into mud soon...

                        Out of the city, oh, West Hill!

The autumnal scenery is let down badly this year!

The bright moon in the mountain, crescent or round:

Who will listen to the poplar's lamentation at dusk?

Who will admire the homeward-bound birds in the wind?

Who will go uphill for a walk, quietly and calmly,

To collect a few leaves in a grove of banyan trees?

Who will dust in the Buddhist temple in the night

To take a good look at the golden faces of the saints?

The mood in sickness: one after another memory

Like mottled clouds cast down by the sky, reflected

Xu Zhimo

In the pool of green water, passing by the ripples;

Like shadows sliding across the white empty corner,

Seemingly there, and in a instant disappearing from sight;

Like wisps of smoke rising from cookers, intermittently...

Like wild geese in the evening sky in no formation

Flying farther and farther away, into the farthest mountain;

Like a meteor in the summer night, a silvery flash

Of light flashing by, impossible to be gazed at for long;

Like the sweet smell of orchids drifting by

Occasionally — who can make the formless stay?

Like the sound of bells from the faraway temple , gone

With the wind, in the spring night, rocking your broken dreams.

A draft unfinished seven years ago completed in May 1931